Tricks Plays Tricks

Written by Jahnna N. Malcolm
Illustrated by Bob Ostrom

HOOKED ON SPANISH™

ISBN 1-933863-03-X

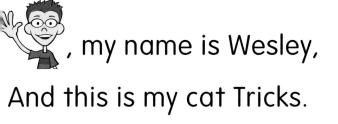 , my name is Wesley,

And this is my cat Tricks.

Tricks sure does love numbers.

Let's see which one he picks.

Hey! Look what Tricks can do!

He turned into a **6**!

Tricks can be so funny

When he climbs a tree.

Watch him turn into a bird
When I count to 3.

1, 2, 3…hello, birdie!

Tricks is acting sneaky

As he tiptoes to my door.

Wonder what Tricks will be

When we count to 4?

1, 2, 3, 4.

Hello, Tricks!

Your costume's really neat.

You're such a good cat.

May I offer you a treat?

Now we're ready for a swim—

Perhaps a big swan dive.

What will Tricks become

When I count to **5**?

1. 2. 3. 4. 5.

Look out below!

Now Tricks is a spaceship

Full of little men.

Want to see what happens
When I count to 10?

1, 2, 3, 4, 5, 6, 7, 8,
9, 10!

Blast off! , Tricks!

Glossary

hola
(OH-lah)
hello

adiós
(ah-DYOHS)
goodbye

tres
(trehs)
three

4

cuatro
(KWAH-troh)
four

1

uno
(OO-noh)
one

cinco
(SEEN-koh)
five

2

dos
(dohs)
two

seis
(sayss)
six

7

siete
(SYEH-tay)
seven

8

ocho
(OH-choh)
eight

9

nueve
(NWEH-bay)
nine

10

diez
(dyehs)
ten